Scott Foresman
SCIENCE

Student Workbook

Grade K

Scott Foresman

Editorial Offices: Glenview, Illinois • New York, New York
Sales Offices: Reading, Massachusetts • Duluth, Georgia • Glenview, Illinois
Carrollton, Texas • Menlo Park, California

www.sfscience.com

Series Authors

Dr. Timothy Cooney
Professor of Earth Science and
  Science Education
Earth Science Department
University of Northern Iowa
Cedar Falls, Iowa

Michael Anthony DiSpezio
Science Education Specialist
Cape Cod Children's Museum
Falmouth, Massachusetts

Barbara K. Foots
Science Education Consultant
Houston, Texas

Dr. Angie L. Matamoros
Science Curriculum Specialist
Broward County Schools
Ft. Lauderdale, Florida

Kate Boehm Nyquist
Science Writer and Curriculum Specialist
Mount Pleasant, South Carolina

Dr. Karen L. Ostlund
Professor
Science Education Center
The University of Texas at Austin
Austin, Texas

Contributing Authors

Dr. Anna Uhl Chamot
Associate Professor and
  ESL Faculty Advisor
Department of Teacher Preparation
  and Special Education
Graduate School of Education
  and Human Development
The George Washington University
Washington, DC

Dr. Jim Cummins
Professor
Modern Language Centre and
  Curriculum Development
Ontario Institute for Studies in Education
Toronto, Canada

Gale Phillips Kahn
Lecturer, Science and Math Education
Elementary Education Department
California State University, Fullerton
Fullerton, California

Vince Sipkovich
Teacher
Irvine United School District
Irvine, California

Steve Weinberg
Science Consultant
Connecticut State Department
  of Education
Hartford, Connecticut

ISBN 0-673-59303-7

Printed in the United States of America

3 4 5 6 7 8 9 0 – PO – 03 02 01 00 99

Contents

© Scott Foresman K

Name_____

© Scott Foresman K

○ Dear Family,

Our class will be learning about living things
and nonliving things. We will learn to identify
living things such as plants and animals and
nonliving things such as toys and rocks.
In the space, I drew a picture that shows
living and nonliving things. On the back of this
page are ideas for activities that you and I
○ can do together to get started learning
about living and nonliving things.

Science at Home

Here are some activities we can do together.

Guessing Game

I'll look around the room and find a living thing.

You ask me questions until you guess it.

Then you find a nonliving thing.

I'll ask you questions to guess it.

Label It

First we'll cut a sheet of paper into four pieces.

Next we'll write yes or no on each piece.

Then I'll put the yes labels on some living things.

Last I'll put the no labels on some nonliving things.

Science in the Community

Help your child "adopt" a living thing found in your neighborhood such as a garden or sidewalk plant. Assist your child in caring for this living thing for several days. During this period, encourage your child to observe and draw pictures of this living thing. Talk about how your child is helping this living thing to meet some of its needs.

Name _____

Living Things I Saw

© Scott Foresman K

Notes for Home Your child colored pictures showing living things.
Home Activity: Ask your child to point to a living thing and tell something about it.

What Living Things Need

 Notes for Home Your child found a picture of a living thing and drew something that this living thing needs.
Home Activity: Ask your child how he or she might help a plant get what it needs.

Explore growing sprouts.

Draw.

1

2

3

4

5

6

Notes for Home Your child drew pictures to show what happens over time to alfalfa seeds that are kept moist.
Home Activity: Use the pictures to talk with your child about how the seeds changed over time.

Nonliving Things in a Home

What nonliving things are in a home?

Notes for Home Your child drew some nonliving things that could be found in a home.
Home Activity: Ask your child to point to a nonliving thing in your home and tell something about it.

Living or Nonliving?

Which things are living?

Color them.

Which things are nonliving?

Do not color them.

Notes for Home Your child colored the living things in this fishbowl.
Home Activity: Ask your child how he or she might care for the living things in this fishbowl.

Name _____

Explore living and nonliving objects.

Draw.

Living	Nonliving

Notes for Home Your child drew pictures to show living and nonliving objects found in a soil sample.
Home Activity: As you walk outside with your child, point to objects and have your child tell if they are living or nonliving.

Name _____

© Scott Foresman K

◯ Dear Family,
Our class will be learning about animals, what animals need, and animal babies. In the space, I drew a picture of an animal I know or like. On the back of this page are some ideas of things we can do together to learn about animals.

Science at Home

Here are some games we can play:

"Animal Riddles"

First listen to these clues.

This animal has

soft fur,

long ears,

and hops.

What is it?

Now you give me a clue.

"Animal Pictionary"

First draw a picture of an animal.

I'll tell you what it is.

Then I'll draw a picture.

You tell me what animal it is.

Science in the Community

When you're out and about with your child, become animal watchers. Observe coverings, movement, and animal interaction. Keep a log of drawings and any interesting facts you and your child learn from your observations.

How Do Animals Move?

Frogs hop.   **Horses run.**   **Pigs walk.**

Birds fly.   **Fish swim.**   **Snakes crawl.**

walk	fly
swim	crawl

Notes for Home Your child drew pictures of animals that move in different ways.
Home Activity: Have your child move like an animal while you guess what the animal is.

Name _____

Animal Coverings

fur

feathers

scales

smooth skin

shell

Notes for Home Your child drew or pasted pictures to show animals with different body coverings.
Home Activity: Ask your child to tell you about each body covering and how it helps the animal.

Explore feathers.

Trial		
1		
2		
3		
4		
5		

Notes for Home Your child made tally marks to show which feather stayed airborne longer for each trial. *Home Activity:* Look outside for birds with your child. Observe and discuss how the feathers look when the birds are flying and when they are resting.

Bird Watch

Notes for Home Your child observed birds and colored to show what he or she observed.
Home Activity: You and your child can look for examples of different bird behavior near your home and talk about what you see.

Name _____

My Pet

Draw a pet.

Draw its food and water.

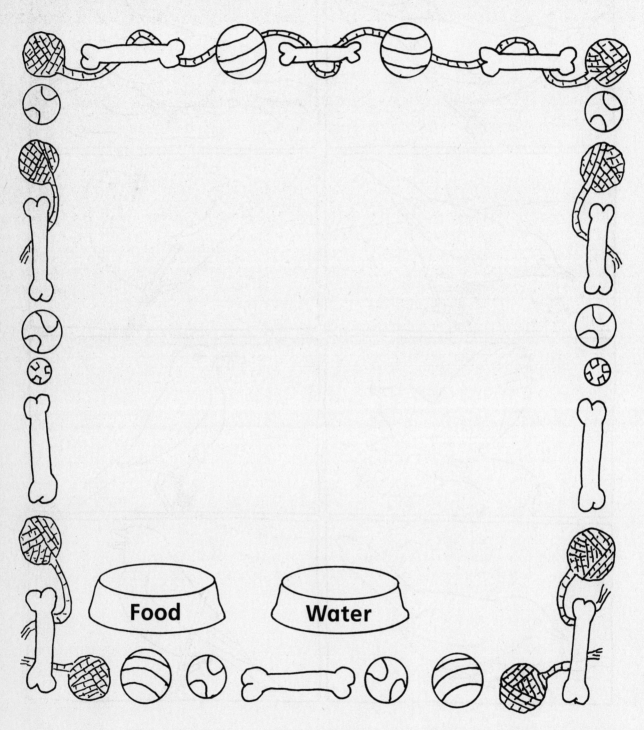

Food

Water

Notes for Home Your child drew a picture of an animal that would be a good pet and the food and water it needs to live.

Home Activity: Talk with your child about a different kind of pet and the things it needs to stay alive.

© Scott Foresman K

Name _____

Explore how feathers protect birds.

Draw.

Notes for Home Your child drew water droplets to show what happens when water is dropped on a feather.
Home Activity: Discuss with your child how feathers protect birds when it rains.

© Scott Foresman K

Animals and Their Babies

adult   baby

A cow is an adult.   A calf is a baby.

Draw.

adult	baby

© Scott Foresman K

Notes for Home Your child drew or cut and pasted a picture of a favorite animal and its baby.
Home Activity: Ask your child to tell how the adult and baby are alike and how they are different.

Name _____

Caring for Baby Animals

Notes for Home Your child drew a picture of one way a favorite animal takes care of its baby.
Home Activity: Ask your child to share more ways the animal could care for its baby.

22 Use with Page A19

Name _____

Explore nests.

Draw.

Notes for Home Your child drew a picture to show a bird nest and how the bird uses the nest to care for its young.
Home Activity: Look for bird nests outside with your child. Talk about what makes a good place for a bird nest.

○ Dear Family,
Our class will be learning about plants. We
will talk about things that plants need to live.
We will learn about seeds, roots, stems, leaves,
and flowers. In the space, I drew some plants.
Look on the other side to find out about
some things that you and I can do together
to find out more about plants.

Science at Home

Here are some activities we can do together.

What's the Plant?

I'll think of a plant that I like.

I'll tell you some things about the plant.

You guess the plant.

Then we'll switch.

Windowsill Garden

We'll save seeds from fruits we eat.

You can help me plant them in soil.

We'll give them water and light.

Then we'll watch them grow.

Science in the Community

The next time you and your child do errands, look indoors and outdoors for plants of all shapes and sizes. Encourage your child to show you the leaves and the stems of different plants. Talk with your child about the importance of plants in your community. How are plants used to make the neighborhood look nice? What other important things do plants provide?

A Sunflower Seed Grows

A sunflower grows.

Look.

Figure out the order.

Use 1, 2, 3, 4 to show the order.

Notes for Home Your child numbered pictures to show how a seed grows into a plant.
Home Activity: Ask your child to point to the picture that shows where seeds for more sunflowers will come from.

Name _____

What Will the Seed Become?

Paste a seed.

Draw the plant.

Notes for Home Your child chose a seed and drew a picture showing the plant that will grow from this seed.
Home Activity: Point to an indoor or outdoor plant. Have your child talk about some changes that happen as the plant grows.

Name _____

Explore how seeds move.

Draw.

Circle.

How My Seed Might Move				
	Seed 1		Seed 2	
Float in air	Yes	No	Yes	No
Float on water	Yes	No	Yes	No
Stick to things	Yes	No	Yes	No

Notes for Home Your child tested seeds to show how they move, then circled to show his or her observations.
Home Activity: After walking outside with your child, look for seeds on your clothing or shoes. Talk about why you did or did not find any seeds.

Experiment with seeds.

Draw.

Experiment With Seeds		
Observe	**Dry**	**Wet**
1		
2		
3		
4		

Notes for Home Your child drew pictures to show what happened to seeds under different conditions.
Home Activity: Look at a growing plant with your child. Talk about what the plant needs to grow.

What a Plant Needs

Draw a plant.

Show something it needs.

© Scott Foresman K

Notes for Home Your child drew a plant that is getting something it needs—air, water, or light.
Home Activity: Talk with your child about things that plants need to stay alive.

Name _____

Helping Plants

Help the plant.

Show how.

Notes for Home Your child drew pictures showing how he or she could help these plants.
Home Activity: You and your child can look for plants around your home and talk about how to care for them.

34 Use with Page A29

© Scott Foresman K

Name _____

Explore moisture.

🌷🌷🌷 The Best Pot for Planting 🌷🌷🌷

Predict		
Observe		

© Scott Foresman K

🎒 **Notes for Home** Your child predicted by marking an X under which flower pot will be the best for planting. Then your child marked an X under which pot will be best for planting based on his or her observations.
Home Activity: Have your child use the pictures to explain which pot is best for planting.

What Plant Parts Are Missing?

Look at each plant.

What part is missing?

Draw it.

Notes for Home Your child drew the missing part of each plant.
Home Activity: The next time you fix a salad, invite your child to show you some plant parts.

© Scott Foresman K

Name _____

Looking at a Leaf

Make a leaf rubbing.

Tell about the leaf.

Notes for Home Your child made this leaf rubbing.
Home Activity: Look at some leaves with your child. Ask your child to tell you how a plant's leaves help it get what it needs.

Explore parts of plants.

Draw.

Parts of Plants			
Roots	Stems	Leaves	Flowers

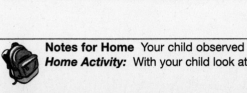

Notes for Home Your child observed plants, then drew pictures to record his or her observations.
Home Activity: With your child look at and discuss these parts of a plant: roots, stems, leaves, and flowers.

Name _____

Dear Family,

Our class will be learning about physical science. We will describe how objects look and feel. We will also be comparing the weight of objects and learning that many objects are made up of different parts. In the space, I drew a picture of a toy to help me talk about how the toy looks, feels, and moves. On the back of this page are ideas for activities that you and I can do together to get started learning about the physical characteristics of objects.

© Scott Foresman K

Science at Home

Here are some activities we can do together.

Touch and Guess

You put something in a paper bag.

I'll reach in and touch it.

I'll use words like <u>soft</u>, <u>hard</u>, <u>smooth</u>, <u>rough</u>, <u>round</u>, <u>square</u>, <u>heavy</u>, or <u>light</u> to tell how it feels.

Then I'll try to guess the object.

Light or Heavy

First we'll write <u>light</u> or <u>heavy</u> on two cards.

Next, you choose two objects.

I'll hold them to decide which weighs more.

Then I'll put a label by each thing.

Last, I'll choose objects, and you take a turn.

Science in the Community

Gas stations, hardware stores, and supermarkets are great places to explore objects. As you do errands with your child, help him or her become aware of different ways to organize and sort objects using their size, shape, color, or weight. Inviting your child to help you sort laundry or put away groceries will reinforce what he or she is learning about objects, too.

Name _____

All About an Object

© Scott Foresman K

Notes for Home Your child drew an object and described its physical characteristics.
Home Activity: Ask your child to point to an object in your home and describe its size, color, and shape and tell about the way it feels.

Name _____

Sorting It All Out

Show a group.

Name it.

© Scott Foresman K

Notes for Home Your child sorted objects and drew a group.
Home Activity: After a meal, involve your child in putting clean dishes or tableware in their proper place.
Talk about how your child knew where each thing belonged.

Name _____

Explore material.

Draw.

Notes for Home Your child drew a sock to show its characteristics such as color and size.
Home Activity: Invite your child to help sort socks the next time you do laundry. Talk about how your child knows which socks make a pair.

Light or Heavy?

Draw something light.
Draw something heavy.

Notes for Home Your child identified light and heavy objects.
Home Activity: When putting away toys, have your child pick up two toys and tell which is lighter and which is heavier.

Lighter or Heavier?

Draw something lighter than your shoe.

Draw something heavier than your shoe.

Then compare the weights of three more things.

Lighter	My Object	Heavier

Notes for Home Your child compared the weights of three objects.
Home Activity: When preparing a meal, give your child an object and invite him or her to find things in the kitchen that are lighter and heavier than that object.

48 Use with Page B9

Name _____

Explore weight.

Draw.

Large Object	Small Objects

© Scott Foresman K

Notes for Home Your child drew pictures to show how many small objects it took to balance a large object.
Home Activity: Talk with your child about how the balance changes when the objects are not balanced.
For example, ask: "How does the scale look when only a block is on it?"

Use with Page B9a **49**

What Part Is Missing?

Draw the missing part.

Notes for Home Your child identified missing parts and drew them.
Home Activity: Invite your child to select a toy. Take turns pointing to and naming the parts of the toy.

Use with Page B11   **51**

Making a Snack

Show the parts.

Show how to make the snack.

1.	**2.**
3.	**4.**

Notes for Home Your child drew the ingredients needed to make a snack and then showed how to combine them.

Home Activity: Involve your child in helping to make a salad. Have him or her identify each ingredient or part. Then talk about how the parts were put together to make the whole salad.

Name _____

Explore parts of toys.

Draw.

 Notes for Home Your child explored toys, then drew one toy and used arrows to show the toy parts that move.
Home Activity: Explore toys at home with your child. Talk about which parts of the toys move and how they move.

○ Dear Family,

Our class will be learning about three forms of energy: sound, heat, and light. We will listen for loud and soft sounds. We will compare hot and cold objects. We will learn about things that make light. In the space, I drew a picture of a fire in a fireplace, then I talked about heat and light from a fire. On the back of this page are ideas for activities that you and I can do together to get

○ started learning about sound, heat, and light.

Science at Home

Here are some activities we can do together.

What's That Sound?

Close your eyes.

Listen to the sound I make.

Guess what I used to make the sound.

Then let's switch roles.

Fun with Sun Tea

First we'll fill a quart jar with cold water.

Then we'll put in 2 caffeine-free tea bags.

Next we'll put the jar in the sun for 4 hours.

We'll try it warm and then cold.

Which way do you like your sun tea?

Science in the Community

Help your child become aware of safety sounds and lights in your community. Fire engine and police sirens warn motorists and pedestrians to move out of the way. Traffic lights at intersections tell us when to stop and go. As you are out and about in your neighborhood, talk with your child about these safety sounds and lights. Encourage your child to tell you what each means, and have him or her show you safe ways to walk in the neighborhood.

Softer or Louder?

Draw.

Softer		Louder

 Notes for Home Your child drew objects that make softer sounds and louder sounds than a person speaking.
Home Activity: Ask your child to point to objects that make a softer sound and a louder sound than your doorbell.

Name _____

Canister Shake

Draw.

Softer	Louder

Notes for Home Your child placed objects in canisters, shook them, and compared the sounds. Then your child drew pictures to show which was softer and which was louder.
Home Activity: Help your child make shakers by putting small objects in clean, empty cans and covering them with foil. Shake to compare two sounds. Which is softer? Which is louder?

Explore sounds.

Draw.

Notes for Home Your child listened to sound-producing objects with and without cylinders and then drew the cylinder and object that created the loudest sound.
Home Activity: Take turns with your child listening to sound-producing objects with and without a cylinder (such as an empty paper towel roll).

Name _____

Is It Hot or Cold?

Draw.

Hot	Cold

Notes for Home Your child drew hot and cold objects.
Home Activity: When eating, ask your child to name some hot foods and some cold foods that are part of the meal.

© Scott Foresman K

Name _____

Changes Caused by Heat and Cold

Draw.

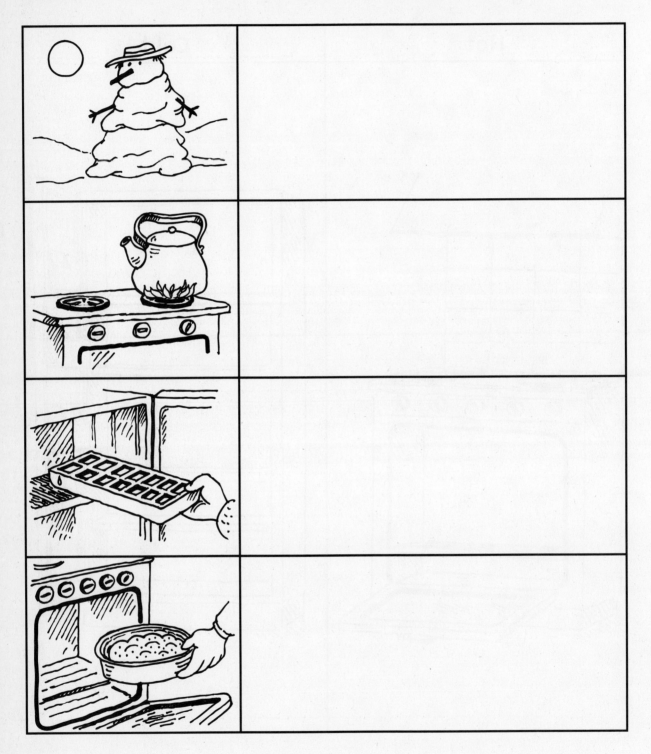

© Scott Foresman K

Notes for Home Your child drew pictures showing how heat and cold can affect objects.
Home Activity: Have your child observe foods before and after cooking or freezing. Talk about how heat and cold change the foods.

Name _____

Explore ice.

Draw.

What I Think	What I See

Notes for Home Your child filled a balloon with liquid and drew a picture to predict what the liquid would look like after it was frozen. After freezing the balloon, your child drew another picture to show how the liquid looked. *Home Activity:* Help your child freeze water in different shape containers. Talk about how the cold affects the liquid.

© Scott Foresman K

Name _____

Inside and Outside Lights

Draw the missing lights.

Notes for Home Your child identified missing indoor and outdoor lights and drew them.
Home Activity: Talk about the different kinds of lights found in your home. Which room has the most lights?

© Scott Foresman K

An Important Light

Color the lights.

Use

red   yellow   green

_____
- - - - - - - - - - - - - - - - -
_____ **means Stop.**

_____
- - - - - - - - - - - - - - - - -
_____ **means Slow.**

_____
- - - - - - - - - - - - - - - - -
_____ **means Go.**

© Scott Foresman K

Notes for Home Your child colored the traffic light.
Home Activity: Point out a traffic light in your neighborhood. Have your child identify the colors and tell what each means.

Explore light.

Paste.

Notes for Home Your child experimented to find out what happens to a paper with a block on it that is left in the sunlight.
Home Activity: Ask your child to point out the shape on the paper pasted on this page and to tell how the shape was made.

Name _____

Experiment with a shadow.

Draw.

Notes for Home Your child drew a picture to show the shadow created when a flashlight was shown on a block or other object.

Home Activity: Look for shadows with your child. Talk about where the light source is in relation to the shadow.

○ Dear Family,

Our class will be learning about different
kinds of movement. We will talk about ways
that objects and people can move. We will
learn about objects that float and those
that sink. We will also explore the way
magnets make some things move. In the space,
I drew a picture that shows a way I like to
move. On the back of this page are ideas for
○ activities that you and I can do together to
find out more about movement.

Science at Home

Here are some activities we can do together.

Copy Cat

Let's stand face-to-face.

I'll make some movements.

You watch and copy them.

Then we'll switch.

Magnet Hunt

How many magnets can we find?

First check the refrigerator door.

Then we can look at cupboards.

If we have letter magnets,

we can make words.

Science in the Community

When riding or walking in the community, point out something that is moving and ask your child to talk about its movement. Encourage your child to look for things that can roll, slide, bounce, or spin. Invite your child to show you ways that he or she can move. What movements are safe to do on a lawn or in a park? What movements are safe on sidewalks or inside stores?

Ways to Move

Show how you move.

She can run.

He can hop.

I can _____.

___

Notes for Home Your child drew and wrote about ways to move.
Home Activity: Turn on some music and ask your child to march, hop, or tiptoe to the beat. After each type of movement, ask: "How did your arms and legs move?"

Ways Toys Move

Test the toy.

Show how it moves.

	Bounce	**Roll**	**Spin**	**Slide**
Ball				
Car				
Block				

© Scott Foresman K

Notes for Home Your child tested toys to see how they move.
Home Activity: Have your child test a toy to see how it moves. Ask: "Does it bounce, roll, spin, or slide?"

Name _____

Explore movement.

Draw.

Notes for Home Your child drew lines to show how high a ball bounces when dropped from different heights. **Home Activity:** Bounce a ball with your child on different surfaces such as grass and cement. Ask: "How does the ball's movement change from one surface to another surface?"

Will It Float or Sink?

Draw things that float.
Draw things that sink.

Notes for Home Your child drew objects that float and sink.
Home Activity: Help your child select objects to test in the sink or bathtub.

Name _____

Sink the Boat.

Draw your boat.

Before

After

 Notes for Home Your child drew a boat before and after sinking it.
Home Activity: Give your child some plastic containers to use in the tub. Talk about how they float and sink.

Name _____

Explore floating
and sinking.

Draw.

Notes for Home Your child drew pictures to show what happens to raisins in water and in a clear carbonated liquid.
Home Activity: Have your child test other small pieces of fruit in a clear, carbonated liquid to see what happens.

What Will a Magnet Pull?

Draw.

Notes for Home Your child drew objects attracted by magnets.
Home Activity: Help your child find magnets around the house, for example, on cabinet doors and the
clasp on a purse.

Name _____

What Can a Magnet Pull Through?

yes　　**no**	**yes**　　**no**
yes　　**no**	**yes**　　**no**

 Notes for Home Your child tested the pull of a magnet through materials such as cloth, paper, plastic, and wood.
Home Activity: Wrap a magnet in foil. Have your child guess and then test if it will attract a paper clip or safety pin through the foil.

Explore pushing and pulling with magnets.

Draw.

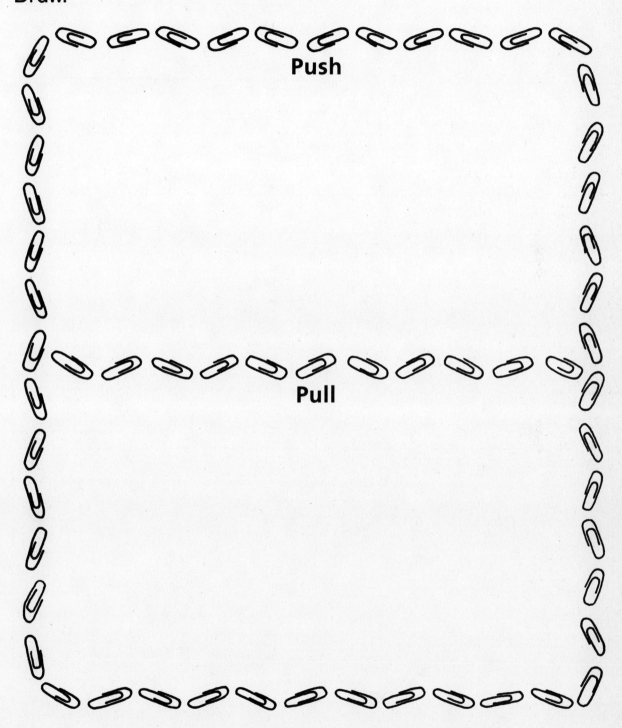

Push

Pull

Notes for Home Your child drew pictures to show magnets push and pull each other.
Home Activity: Have your child use a magnet to show how it can pull things such as a paper clip.

Name_____

○ Dear Family,
Our class will be learning about Earth and the
sky. We will talk about landforms and bodies
of water. We will also learn about things seen
in the daytime sky and the nighttime sky. I
drew a picture of a place where I would like
to hike. Look on the other side to find out
about things that you and I can do together
○ to find out more about Earth and the sky.

© Scott Foresman K

Science at Home

Here are some activities we can do together. ◯

Moon Walk

We can look at the moon
each night for a week.
I'll draw what I see.
We can talk about how the moon seems to change.

Pictures in the Sky

We can look at clouds in the sky. ◯

What shapes or pictures do we see?

How do the clouds move and change?

What other things can we see in the sky?

Science in the Community

When traveling around your community, alert your
child to some of the landforms and bodies of
water that are present. Depending on where you
live, you may be able to point out hills, valleys,
mountains, plains, lakes, rivers, or streams. If
possible, take photographs of these features.
Your child can use them to make a scrapbook of
your area. With your help, he or she can label
each body of water and landform and share the
scrapbook with other family members. ◯

Nearby Landforms

Draw.

Notes for Home Your child drew and labeled two landforms in your community.
Home Activity: If possible, visit these landforms with your child. Talk about what you observe.

Name _____

Visiting a Body of Water

Draw.

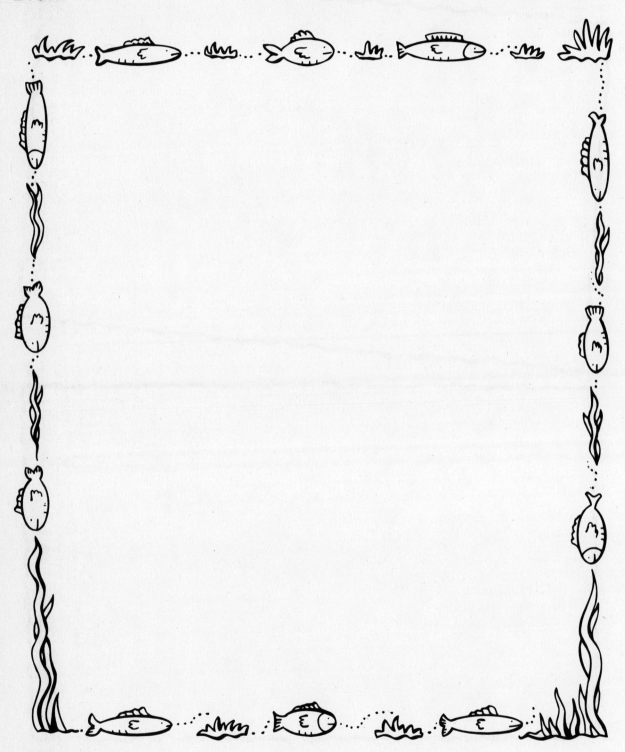

_____

Notes for Home Your child drew and labeled a body of water.
Home Activity: If possible, take your child to visit a nearby lake, river, or stream.

Name _____

Explore water flow.

Draw.

red   yellow   blue

 Notes for Home Your child used a different color to show the water flow after water was poured from the top of a landform three different times.
Home Activity: Have your child pour water over various tub toys and talk about how the water flows.

Things I Saw in the Daytime Sky

Color.

Draw.

Notes for Home Your child colored and drew objects that he or she saw while looking at the sky.
Home Activity: Look out a window with your child. Take turns naming things that you see in the daytime sky.

Name _____

My Daytime Activities

Draw.

Early Morning

Noon

© Scott Foresman K

Notes for Home Your child drew pictures to show where the sun can be seen in the morning and at noon.
Home Activity: If possible, watch a sunrise or a sunset with your child. Talk about where the sun can
be seen in the sky. How does the sky change?

Name _____

Explore the sky.

Draw.

Notes for Home Your child used a viewer and then drew pictures of what was observed in the daytime sky.

Home Activity: Ask your child to model how to use a paper towel roll as a viewer. Take turns using the viewer and talking about what you see.

Name _____

The Nighttime Sky
Draw.

 Notes for Home Your child drew objects that he or she might see in the nighttime sky.
Home Activity: If possible, view the night sky with your child. Talk about what you observe.

Name _____

Daytime and Nighttime

Draw.

 Notes for Home Your child drew and labeled daytime and nighttime pictures.
Home Activity: Have your child look out the same window during the day and again after dark. Talk about
how the sky and the view seem to change.

Name _____

Explore star patterns.

Make dots.

Draw.

Notes for Home Your child made and then connected dots to show star patterns.
Home Activity: If possible, on a clear dark night, look for and talk about star patterns with your child.

© Scott Foresman K

Dear Family,

Our class will be learning about weather and seasons. We will talk about different weather and how weather affects what people wear and do. We will also learn about the four seasons. In the space, I drew a picture of my favorite time of year. The other side has ideas for things that you and I can do together to find out more about the weather and the seasons.

Science at Home

Here are some activities we can do together. ○

A TV Weather Forecast

We can watch a weather forecast on the news.

The next day we can observe the weather.

Was the forecast right?

Did the weather differ from the forecast?

Family Fun in Different Seasons ○

I'll fold a paper in four to make a little book.

We can talk about how our family has fun

each season. I'll draw four pictures to show this.

You can help me write <u>spring</u>, <u>summer</u>, <u>fall</u>,

and <u>winter</u>.

Science in the Community ○

When traveling around your community, alert
your child to symbols in the community that help people
stay informed about weather. For example, point out time
and temperature displays on a local bank. Also look for
natural and man-made signs of the seasons. For example,
in the fall you might help your child notice the leaves
changing color or the type of seasonal clothing on display
in store windows.

© Scott Foresman K

What's the Weather?

Show the weather.

The weather is _____.

The weather is _____.

© Scott Foresman K

Notes for Home Your child drew and labeled pictures showing two types of weather.
Home Activity: Talk about today's weather. How does it compare to yesterday's weather?

What Will I Wear?

Draw.

Notes for Home Your child drew what he or she would wear on a hot sunny day and on a rainy day.
Home Activity: Have your child tell about today's weather and what he or she should wear today.

Explore waterproof material.

Draw. gray

1

2

3

4

Notes for Home Your child tested fabric, then recorded the size of the water spot.
Home Activity: Help your child test a brown paper bag and a plastic bag to see which is more
waterproof. Talk about which bag would make a better makeshift rain poncho.

My Favorite Season

Write.

Draw.

_____

- -

Dear _____,

_____

- -

This shows _____ **where I live.**

Your friend,

_____

- -

_____

Notes for Home Your child drew and wrote about his or her favorite season.
Home Activity: Have your child name another season and describe it.

Name _____

My Daily Weather Record

Draw.

Notes for Home Your child drew symbols to show the weather for five days.
Home Activity: Look at the weather report in the local newspaper. Talk with your child about the
weather symbols.

106 Use with Page C19

Explore evaporation.

Draw.

Day 1   **Day 2**   **Day 3**

© Scott Foresman K

Notes for Home Your child talked about evaporation and drew water to show how the water level in a glass changed each day.
Home Activity: The next time it rains, look for puddles with your child. Notice the size of the puddle, then go back later and talk about how the puddle has changed.

Name_____

○ Dear Family,

Our class will be learning about caring for
the earth. We will find out about natural
resources, such as air, water, soil, forests,
and oil. We will also talk about how people can
conserve and recycle these natural resources.
In the space, I drew a picture showing one of
the earth's resources. The other side of this
○ letter has ideas for things that you and I can
do together to find out more about how
people can care for the earth.

© Scott Foresman K

Name_____

Science at Home

Here are some activities we can do together.

Saving Electricity

I can make signs reminding us to turn off lights.

We can also work together to dust lightbulbs.

Clean bulbs use less energy than dirty ones!

Recycling Shopping Bags

I'll decorate some supermarket bags.

We can reuse the bags when we buy groceries.

We can reuse the bags when we do other errands.

I'll remember to say, "No thanks!" to bags I don't need.

Science in the Community

Talk with your child about recycling in your community. Help him or her identify items that can be recycled from your household. You might work together to set up bins for sorting these items.

Put Your Stamp on It

Draw.

Notes for Home Your child designed a postage stamp showing a natural resource.
Home Activity: Ask your child to tell why this natural resource is important.

© Scott Foresman K

Name _____

Ways We Use Wood
Draw.

Notes for Home Your child drew objects made of wood, which is an important natural resource.
Home Activity: Have your child look around your home and identify some objects made from wood.

Explore oil and water.

Draw.

Notes for Home Your child drew a picture to show what happens when you try to mix oil and water.
Home Activity: The next time you are at a gas station with your child, ask a mechanic to explain how to dispose of used oil so it does not get dumped into local water.

Energy Pledge

Draw.

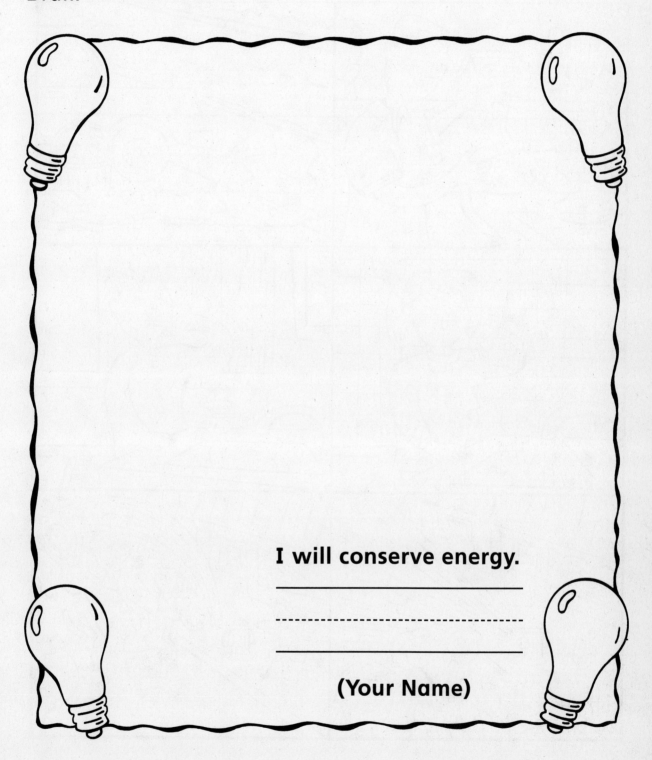

I will conserve energy.

_____

- -

_____

(Your Name)

Notes for Home Your child drew something that he or she could do to conserve energy.
Home Activity: Encourage your child to share this energy pledge with other family members.

Name _____

Conserving Water

Notes for Home Your child colored pictures to show water savers and crossed out pictures to show water wasters.
Home Activity: Ask your child to tell you how people can save water while brushing their teeth.

116 Use with Page C27

Name _____

Explore water flow.

Draw.

Notes for Home Your child drew pictures to show water flow through a pin hole when the top is on the bottle and when the top is off the bottle.
Home Activity: Help your child learn to turn a water faucet handle to control water flow. Discuss how the water should be flowing from the faucet to help conserve water.

Experiment with filtering water.

Draw.

Paper

Pebbles

Notes for Home Your child drew pictures to show how dirty water looked after it was filtered through paper and through pebbles.
Home Activity: Talk with your child about other filters such as a furnace filter. Ask: "Why do you think a furnace has a filter?"

Name _____

Let's Recycle!

Draw.

Notes for Home Your child labeled each bin and then drew pictures to show what can be recycled.
Home Activity: Suggest your child decorate a small box for recycling paper, then use the blank side of
the paper from the recycling box for phone messages and notes.

Name _____

Treasures from Trash

Draw.

Notes for Home Your child drew something made from recycled items.
Home Activity: Involve your child in recycling small boxes, cans, and plastic cartons at home.

Name _____

Explore packaging.

Draw.

No packaging	1 package	2 or more packages

© Scott Foresman K

Notes for Home Your child evaluated product packaging and drew pictures to show how some products are packaged.
Home Activity: The next time you go food shopping with your child, ask: "Which of our groceries have the least packaging."

Name_____

○ Dear Family,

Our class will be learning about the senses.
We will use our senses to describe objects. In
the space, I drew a picture of my favorite
food. I can tell how it looks, tastes, smells,
sounds, and feels when I eat it. The other side
of this letter has ideas for things that you
and I can do together to find out more about
○ the senses.

Science at Home

Here are some activities we can do together.

Mystery Box

You close your eyes.

I'll put something in a box.

To guess what it is, you can touch, smell, or listen.

Then we can switch places.

Hide and Find

You hide and then keep whispering my name.

I will use my sense of hearing to find you.

Then we'll switch–I will hide and you

will find me.

Science in the Community

Take a "my senses" walk with your child in your neighborhood. While walking, encourage your child to describe what he or she sees, hears, smells, and touches. After your walk, encourage your child to draw pictures about your community.

Name _____

Ways of Seeing

Draw.

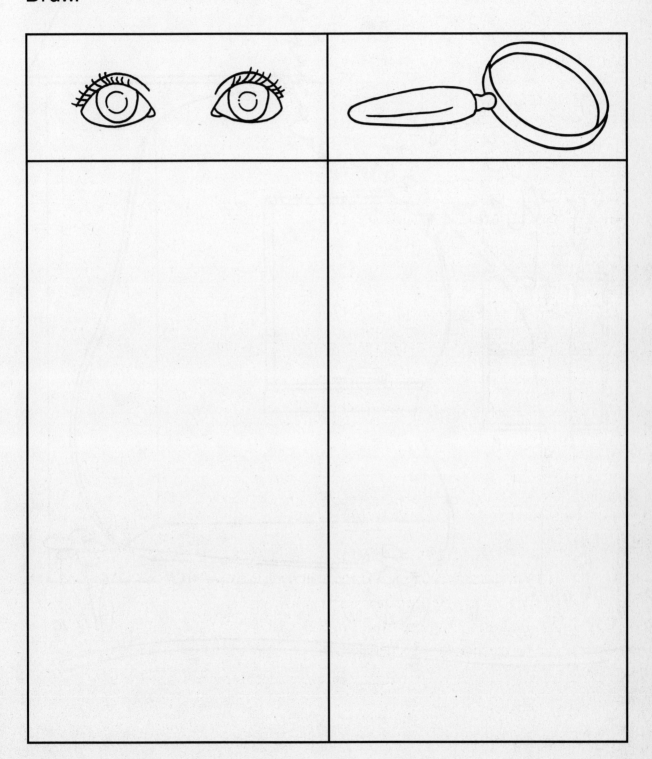

© Scott Foresman K

Notes for Home Your child drew pictures to show how an object looks with his or her eyes and then with a hand lens.
Home Activity: Have your child choose an object and describe its color, shape, and size.

Name _____

Sounds Around Us

Listen, then draw.

© Scott Foresman K

 Notes for Home Your child drew pictures of things making sounds heard inside and outside our classroom.
Home Activity: Have your child look around your home and identify objects that make loud, soft, high, or low sounds.

Name _____

Explore the sense of sight.

Mark.

Notes for Home Your child made marks to show where the bean bag landed after each toss.
Home Activity: Play a game such as "Pin the Tail on the Donkey" with your child and talk about the importance of eye sight.

Name _____

What a Smell!

 Notes for Home Your child colored things that have pleasant odors and crossed out things that have unpleasant odors.
Home Activity: Have your child name several things that have a pleasant odor.

© Scott Foresman K

Name _____

Snack Food Tastes

Draw.

Notes for Home Your child drew or cut and pasted pictures of snacks with different tastes.
Home Activity: Ask your child to name foods that are family favorites. Help your child use words such as *sweet*, *sour*, *salty*, or *spicy* to describe the taste of each food.

Name _____

Explore apples.

Draw.

Write.

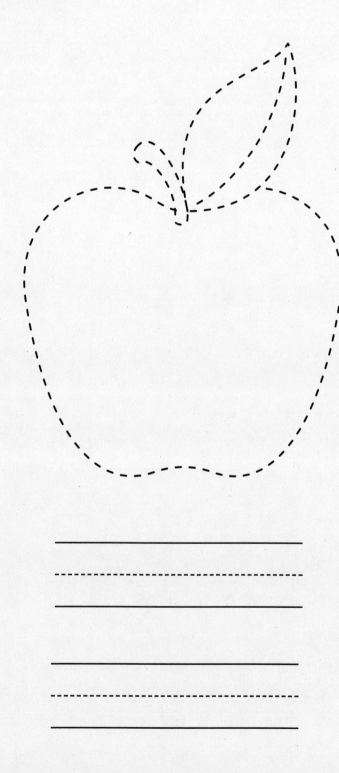

_____

- -

_____

_____

- -

_____

Notes for Home Your child wrote or dictated words to show how he or she can use the senses to gather information about an apple.
Home Activity: The next time you and your child eat a vegetable, such as a carrot or green pepper, help your child use his or her senses to explore and talk about the vegetable.

Name _____

Feeling a Mystery Object

Draw what you felt.

Write about it.

I felt a _____.

It felt _____.

Notes for Home Your child used the sense of touch to identify a mystery object.
Home Activity: Place one small object with a distinct texture in a pillowcase and ask your child to describe and then identify the object using only the sense of touch.

© Scott Foresman K

Name _____

Sorting by Texture

Draw your groups.

_____

_____

_____

_____

Notes for Home Your child drew two groups of objects sorted by texture.
Home Activity: When you are folding laundry, invite your child to sort the items by texture. Talk about
how each item feels.

© Scott Foresman K

Name _____

Explore
Activity
Unit D Chapter 1

Explore textures.

Draw.

Soft	
Smooth	
Rough	
Hard	

© Scott Foresman K

 Notes for Home Your child matched objects with like textures by drawing what was in the bag and by drawing another object with like texture.
Home Activity: Help your child find something smooth and something rough. Touch each object and talk about how they feel different.

Use with Page D11a **137**

$$1 + 1 = 2$$

○ Dear Family,

Our class will be learning about some parts of the body and how we use these parts. We will also find out more about how people grow and change and ways people are alike and different. In the space, I drew a picture of something I can do now that I couldn't do a year ago. The other side of this letter has ideas for things that you and I can do

○ together to find out more about ways people grow and change over time.

Science at Home

Here are some activities we can do together.

Look at Me Grow

We can look at some photos of me.

You can tell me how old I was.

I can put the photos in order.

We can talk about how I've grown!

I Can Do It!

I can do many new things.

I'll act one out for you to guess.

I'll tell you how I learned to do it.

Then I'll share something I want to learn to do.

Science in the Community

As you're out and about in your neighborhood, play an "I Spy" game with your child in which you look for people at different stages of life. Talk with your child about ways that people are alike and different.

Name _____

A Puppet Like Me

Draw.

Notes for Home Your child drew missing parts to complete a puppet.
Home Activity: Play a game such as "Simon Says" in which you name different parts of the body for your child to identify.

© Scott Foresman K

Name _____

Using Your Body

Circle.

 Notes for Home Your child identified which parts of the body are used in certain activities.
Home Activity: Invite your child to tell you what body parts he or she uses when picking up toys, making a bed, or sweeping the floor.

Name _____

Explore balance
and body parts.

Circle.
Underline.

more time   less time

more time   less time

more time   less time

more time   less time

Notes for Home Your child explored balancing for one minute using different body parts. Your child circled each prediction and underlined each result.
Home Activity: With your child, try balancing a book on your heads and walking the length of a hallway. Talk about what parts of the body had to work together to balance the book.

Then and Now

Draw.

Write.

_____

- -

Then I could _____.

_____

- -

Now I can _____.

Notes for Home Your child drew and wrote about being a baby and being himself or herself now.
Home Activity: Invite your child to talk with you about something that he or she would like to be able to do next year.

Name _____

Growing Up

Order.

Baby

Child

Adult

© Scott Foresman K

Notes for Home Your child identified the three stages of life by drawing lines to show which picture should be in which picture frame.
Home Activity: If possible, look at family pictures with your child and talk about the three stages of life: baby, child, and adult.

146 Use with Page D19

Name _____

Explore teeth.

Color.

 Notes for Home Your child colored to show the effect cola can have on teeth.
Home Activity: Help your child make and post a chart near the bathroom sink for recording each time
he or she brushes teeth.

Lend a Hand

Press.

Notes for Home Your child compared the size of his or her hand with that of a friend.
Home Activity: Have your child place the palm of his or her hand against yours. How are your hands alike? How are they different?

Name _____

What I Like to Do

Draw.

Write.

_____

- -

I like to _____.

Notes for Home Your child drew and wrote about a special interest.
Home Activity: Talk about something that you enjoyed doing as a child. If possible, you and your child
might have fun doing this activity together.

Name _____

Explore fingerprints.

Press.

Notes for Home Your child made his or her fingerprints, then used a hand lens to observe the pattern in the fingerprints.

Home Activity: Examine your fingerprints with your child by shining a bright flashlight on your finger tips. Talk about the patterns.

Dear Family,

Our class will learn about things we can do to stay healthy. We will explore ways to keep fit by exercising and resting. We will also talk about foods we need to grow and stay healthy. In the space, I drew a picture of something I do to stay healthy. The other side of this letter has ideas for things you and I can do together to find out more about staying healthy.

Name _____

Science at Home

Here are some activities we can do together.

Guess My Fruit or Vegetable

I'll give you hints about a mystery food.

I'll tell you its color, its size, and its shape.

I'll tell you if it is a fruit or vegetable.

After you figure out my mystery food,

you can think up one for me to guess.

Soapy Crayons

You can pour 1/8 cup of water into a cup.

Then I will fill the cup with soap flakes

(be sure they are flakes).

After mixing it up, I will add food coloring.

We can spoon the mixture into an ice cube tray.

We'll let the cubes dry for one or two days.

Then I can use the soap crayons in the tub!

Science in the Community

The next time the two of you grocery shop, spend time in the produce section. What fruits and vegetables can your child identify? Are there new ones the two of you would like to try? Talk about why hand washing is important before preparing or eating any food.

© Scott Foresman K

Ways to Exercise

Draw.

Write.

_____

- -

I like to _____ .

_____

- -

I like to _____ .

© Scott Foresman K

Notes for Home Your child drew and wrote about favorite ways to exercise indoors and outdoors. *Home Activity:* Have your child keep an exercise log for a week by drawing pictures showing how he or she exercised.

Ways to Rest

Draw.

Write.

Notes for Home Your child drew ways to rest.
Home Activity: Invite your child to tell you why it is important to get a good night's sleep. Talk about things that help your child fall asleep.

Name _____

Explore heartbeat.

Draw.

Notes for Home Your child drew pictures to show how different activities affect the heartbeat.
Home Activity: Take a brisk walk with your child around your neighborhood. As you walk, encourage your child to notice changes in his or her heartbeat and to look for other activities people do that might affect their heartbeats.

What's for Lunch?

Color.

Circle.

Draw.

_____   _____

- - - - - - - - - - - -   - - - - - - - - - - - -

I like _____ and _____ for lunch.

Notes for Home Your child colored fruits, circled vegetables, then drew one of each to complete a lunch.
Home Activity: Invite your child to tell what he or she likes to eat for lunch on a school day. Does this lunch include at least one serving of a fruit or a vegetable?

Name _____

Planning a Meal

Draw.

 Notes for Home Your child drew foods to show a balanced meal made up of foods from at least three food groups.

Home Activity: At your next family meal, invite your child to identify several foods and tell in which food group each belongs.

Explore healthful foods.

Draw.

My Healthful Food	

Notes for Home Your child drew four characteristics of one healthful food.
Home Activity: During the week, help your child select and prepare a favorite healthful snack.

Name _____

Experiment with foods.

Draw.

Fat	No Fat

Notes for Home Your child tested foods and drew pictures to show which foods contain fat and which foods contain little or no fat.
Home Activity: With your child, test a favorite family snack for fat.

Rub and Scrub

Draw.

Number.

Notes for Home Your child completed and then sequenced pictures that show proper hand-washing procedures.

Home Activity: Invite your child to show you what he or she has learned about hand-washing.

Name _____

Hidden Tools

Color.

![backpack icon] **Notes for Home** Your child found five hidden health care tools in the picture.
Home Activity: Have your child name each health care tool and tell how it is used
to help people stay healthy.

Explore dirty hands.

Draw.

Touched

**Not
Touched**

Notes for Home Your child drew pictures to show how a bread slice that was not touched by dirty hands looked and how a bread slice that was touched by dirty hands looked after several days.
Home Activity: Talk with your child about times when handwashing is important.

My Process Skills Book

Name_____

Observing

see

hear

smell

taste

touch

Notes for Home Your child matched the senses to the appropriate body parts.
Home Activity: Make up rhymes related to the senses and have your child point to the body part to complete the rhyme. For example: To smell a rose, I use my ____.

Science Process Skill **3**

Name_____

Practice Observing

| see | hear | touch | taste | smell |

Color.

Notes for Home Your child described the pictures by talking about how each object might look, sound, smell, taste, and feel.
Home Activity: At dinner, take turns describing the food by telling how each item looks, sounds, smells, tastes, and feels.

Name_____

Communicating

 Notes for Home Your child drew and described a classroom object to practice communicating information.
Home Activity: Have your child draw a picture of an object in your home, show you the picture, and describe the object.

Name_____

Practice Communicating

Notes for Home Your child described the object in the picture above for members of the class to guess. *Home Activity:* Ask your child to look in a drawer at home and describe one object for you to guess.

© Scott Foresman K

Classifying

 Notes for Home Your child looked at groups of objects and told why the objects were grouped together. *Home Activity:* Look through kitchen cupboards or drawers with your child and talk about how objects are grouped together.

Name _____

Practice Classifying

Draw a line to match.

Round

Soft

Toy

Notes for Home Your child drew lines to match pictures with words that describe them.
Home Activity: The next time you and your child are cleaning up toys, ask your child to sort the toys into groups. Point to two toys and invite your child to tell you why he or she placed those two objects in the same group.

Estimating and Measuring

_____

_____

_____

© Scott Foresman K

Notes for Home Your child estimated how many blocks long each object is and recorded his or her idea by drawing that number of blocks or by writing a number.
Home Activity: The next time you and your child are setting the table for dinner, have your child estimate how many forks wide the dinner table is; then help your child measure to find out.

Name_____

Practice Estimating and Measuring

Draw.

_____

_____

_____

© Scott Foresman K

Notes for Home Your child used blocks to measure each object, then he or she drew that number of blocks under each object or wrote the number next to each object to record his or her measurements. **Home Activity:** Ask your child to estimate how many pennies long a piece of paper is, then help your child use a penny to measure the paper.

10 Science Process Skill

Inferring

Notes for Home Your child traced the lines from the shapes to the boxes and talked about how the shapes and the boxes relate to one another.
Home Activity: Talk about and feel the shape of three vegetables with your child. Place one in a bag, then invite your child to feel the object and infer which vegetable it is.

Name_____

Practice Inferring

Color.

© Scott Foresman K

Notes for Home Your child used touch to infer what shape was hidden in a box, then colored the shape to record his or her inference.
Home Activity: Invite your child to tell you how he or she knew which shape was hidden in the box.

Name_____

Predicting

Circle.

© Scott Foresman K

Notes for Home Your child predicted whether each object weighs more or less than a block and then circled objects he or she predicted weighs more than a block.
Home Activity: Ask your child: "What does it mean to predict? What information did you use to help you predict if an object weighs more or less than a block?"

Name_____

Practice Predicting
Circle.

© Scott Foresman K

Notes for Home Your child tested each object to see if it weighs more or less than a block and then circled each object that weighs more than a block.
Home Activity: Have your child build on the information gathered from this experience to predict if a marker weighs more or less than a block. Ask: "How can we find out?"

Making Definitions

 Notes for Home Your child traced lines to show what each animal might eat, where it might live, and what it might sound like.
Home Activity: Ask your child to tell you about the cat and the dog. Then have your child explain how the cat and dog are alike and how they are different.

Practice Making Definitions

Draw.

 Notes for Home Your child drew and discussed a picture of an animal based on a partner's description of the animal.
Home Activity: Play "What's my object?" with your child. Take turns describing an object and guessing what is being described. Talk about how the clues help the person guessing identify the object.

Name_____

Making and Using Models

Circle.

How many legs?	2	4	6	8

Does it have a tail?   yes   no

Draw.

Notes for Home Your child described and drew a picture of a pet based on that description.
Home Activity: With your child, look around the house for objects that model real objects such as a toy car. Discuss how the toy car is like a real car and different from a real car.

Name_____

Practice Making and Using Models

 Notes for Home Your child made a clay model of a pet and then drew a picture of the pet based on the clay model.

Home Activity: Help your child mold tinfoil to make a model of a kitchen aid such as a saucepan. Display the model next to the real object and discuss how they are alike and how they are different.

Giving Hypotheses

Notes for Home Your child asked questions about whether the eraser will float and then showed his or her hypothesis by circling a picture.
Home Activity: The next time you and your child are doing dishes, show your child an item, such as a sponge. Have your child ask questions and state a hypothesis about whether the sponge will float.

Practice Giving Hypotheses

Draw the eraser.

Notes for Home Your child tested an eraser to see if it floats in water and then drew a picture to show the results.
Home Activity: The next time your child is taking a bath, have your child ask questions and state a hypothesis about whether the soap will float. Test to find out.

Name_____

Collecting Data

Number of Boys   ## Number of Girls

Notes for Home Your child counted and recorded the number of boys and girls in his or her group. **Home Activity:** While you and your child are riding in the car, help your child count and record the number or red cars and the number of blue cars you see during your ride.

Practice Collecting Data

Color.

8		
7		
6		
5		
4		
3		
2		
I		
	Boys	Girls

Notes for Home Your child made and drew a block graph to show the number of boys and girls in his or her group.
Home Activity: Have your child use the graph to answer these questions: "Are there more boys or girls in your group? How do you know?"

Controlling Variables

Notes for Home Your child drew a picture of an ice cube at the beginning of a twenty-minute observation period.
Home Activity: Invite your child to describe the experiment. Ask: "Will the temperature stay the same? (yes) Will the location stay the same? (yes) Will the time stay the same? (no) What do you think will happen?"

Name _____

Practice Controlling Variables

ice cube after 5 minutes

ice cube after 10 minutes

ice cube after 15 minutes

ice cube after 20 minutes

© Scott Foresman K

Notes for Home Your child drew pictures to show how an ice cube looks at five-minute intervals when it is at a constant temperature.
Home Activity: The next time you bake a cake with your child, point out that the temperature and location stay the same, only the time changes. Observe the cake at ten-minute intervals and talk about how the cake changes over time.

Name_____

Experimenting

Circle.

 + =

 + =

Notes for Home Your child circled pictures to show what he or she thinks will happen if oil or sugar is added to water.
Home Activity: Ask your child what he or she thinks will happen if you add one tablespoon of a liquid, such as syrup, to a cup of water. Experiment to find out.

Practice Experimenting

Draw.

Notes for Home Your child drew pictures to show what happened when he or she added sugar to water. *Home Activity:* Ask your child to predict what will happen if salt is added to water. Discuss why, then experiment to find out.

Acknowledgements

Elizabeth Allen 128, 166; **Teresa Anderko** 87- 89, 91, 93, 95-97, 101-103, 105-107, 111-113, 115-117, 119, 121-123; **Ilja Bereznickas** 4, 5, 22, 27, 29, 34, 35, 44, 49, 51, 58, 61, 62, 66, 69, 75, 81, 125, 132, 137, 160; **Jane Caminos** 18, 19, 23, 28, 33, 37-39, 135, 149, 157; **Rita Lascaro** 7, 65, 128, 131, 133, 136, 141, 146, 147, 155, 156, 159, 166; **Dana Regan** 3, 53, 63, 145, 149, 150; **Zina Saunders** 1, 2, 8, 11-15, 17, 21, 25, 26, 41-43, 45, 47, 48, 52, 55-57, 59, 67, 71-74, 77-79, 82, 83, 85, 86, 99, 100, 109, 110, 125-127, 129, 139, 140, 142, 143, 151, 153, 154, 165, 167; Science Process Skills **Dana Regan** 2-9, 11, 12, 14-21, 23, 25, 26